Guide for Parents

Children develop significantly during early childhood. From infancy to the age of 6, many milestones will occur. One such milestone is learning first words. By using this workbook, children can learn to recognize and write 100 of the most common first words in the English language.

As your child progresses, the activities progress as well. This workbook begins with learning to write the lowercase and uppercase letters of the alphabet. Then, simple words are paired with images to help with word recognition. Lastly, there is a recall activity in which images are shown and your child is asked to write the word for each image.

Holding a Pencil

Before getting started, there are a few things your child will need to understand, such as how to hold a pencil. Encourage your child to relax their hand and grip the pencil between the thumb and index finger. Pencil control is an important skill to master. See the images below for the best way to hold the pencil if your child is left-handed or right-handed.

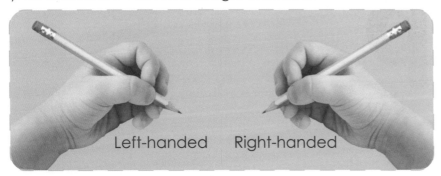

Left-handed   Right-handed

Posture

It is best to sit up straight, at a desk or table, with both feet flat on the floor. Position the workbook at a slight angle depending on your child's dominant hand. Angle to the left for right-handers and slightly to the right for left-handers.

Now, let's get started.

Lowercase Letters

Below are the letters of the alphabet.
Directional arrows show where to start each letter.

a b c d e f

g h i j k l m

n o p q r s t

u v w x y z

Letter Practice

Following the guide on the previous page, practice writing the letters yourself by tracing the letters below.

Uppercase Letters

Uppercase letters are also known as capital letters. These are used to start a sentence and when writing proper nouns, such as your name. Pay attention to the directional arrows and the height of each letter below.

A B C D E F G

H I J K L M

N O P Q R S T

U V W X Y Z

Letter Practice

Following the guide on the previous page, practice writing the letters yourself by tracing the letters below.

ANIMALS

ANIMALS

dog

dog

cat

cat

turtle

fish

rabbit

7

lion

lion

hippo

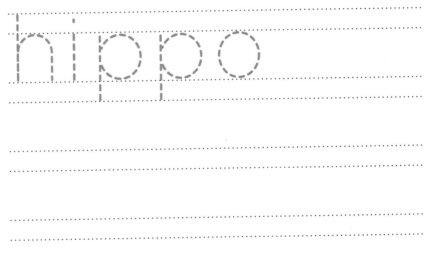

hippo

elephant

elephant

bear

bear

giraffe

giraffe

monkey

monkey

cow

horse

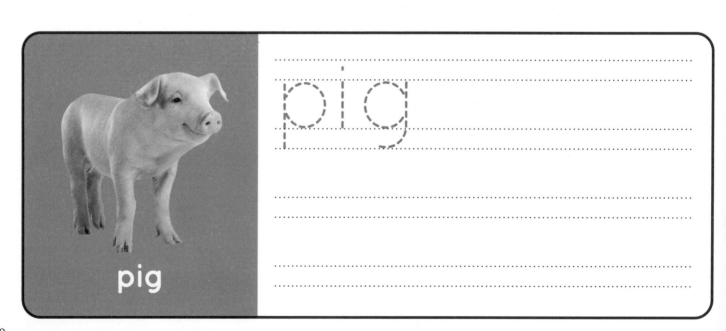

pig

sheep

goat

chicken

Spelling

Can you remember all the words you just learned?
Look at the pictures below. Now, write the animal
words. Keep practicing until you get it right.

COW

FOOD AND DRINK

FOOD AND DRINK

milk

milk

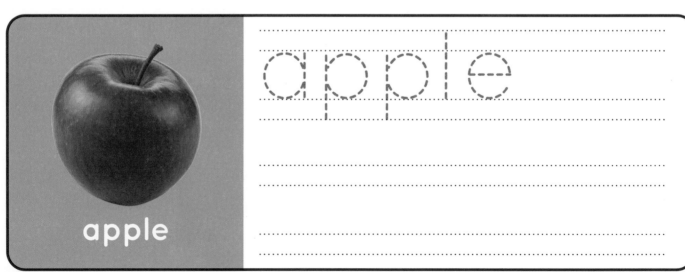

apple

apple

cookie

cheese

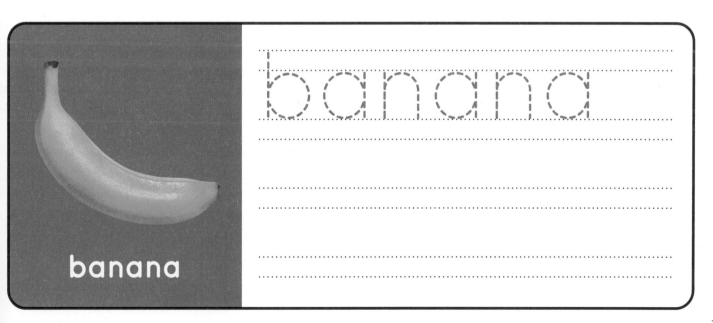

banana

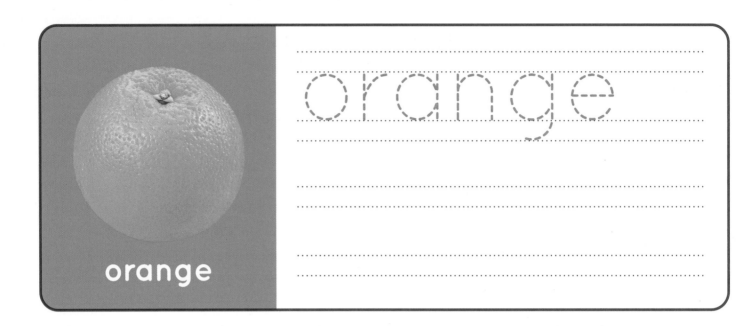

orange

broccoli

cereal

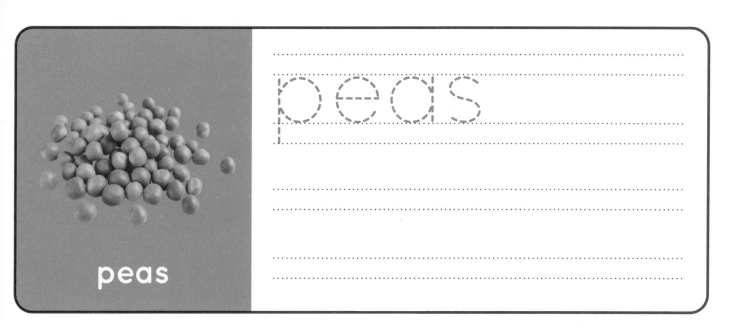

peas

peas

pizza

pizza

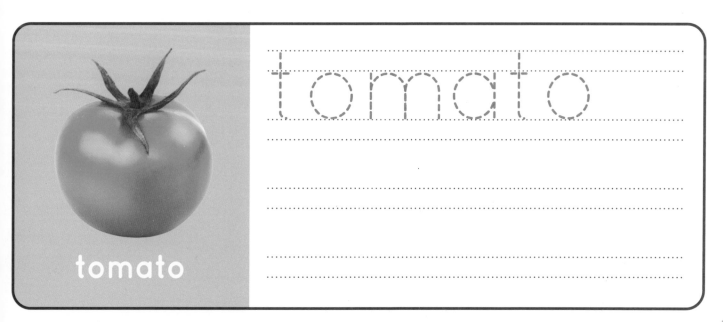

tomato

tomato

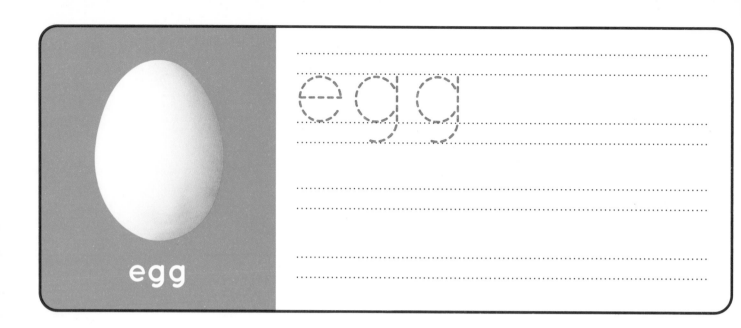

egg

egg

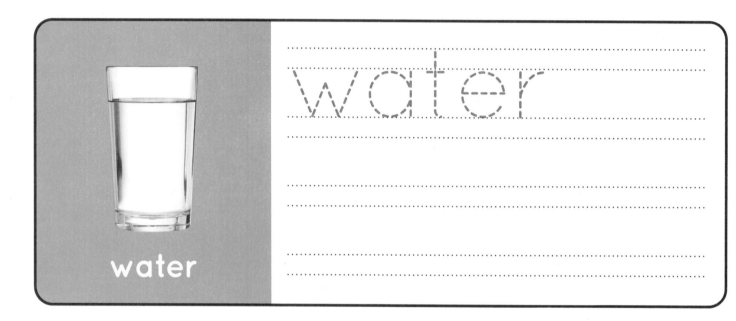

water

water

pasta

pasta

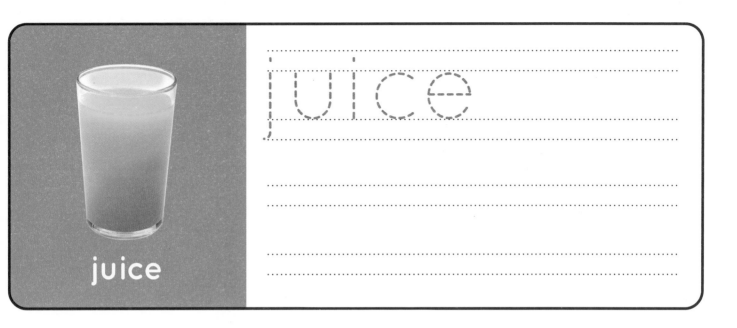

juice

bread

cake

Spelling

Can you remember all the words you just learned?
Look at the pictures below. Now, write the food and drink
words. Keep practicing until you get it right.

peas

AT HOME

AT HOME

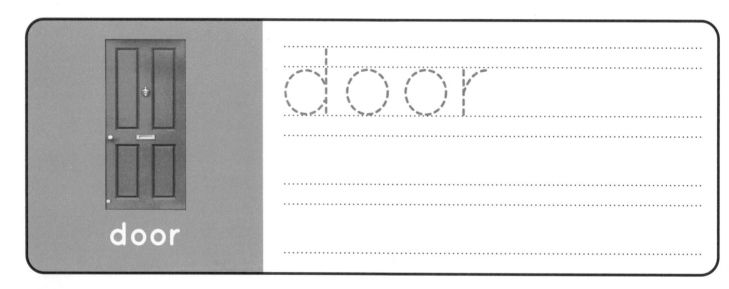

door

window

table

couch

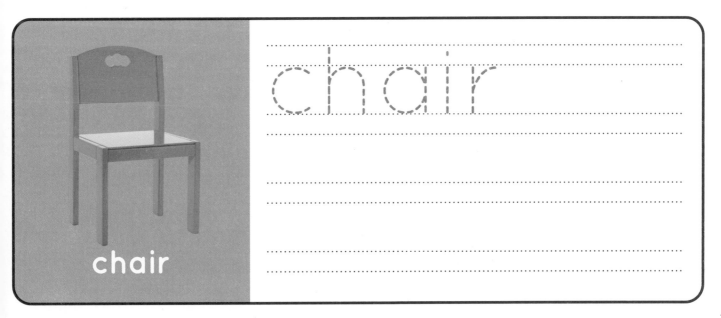

chair

clock

clock

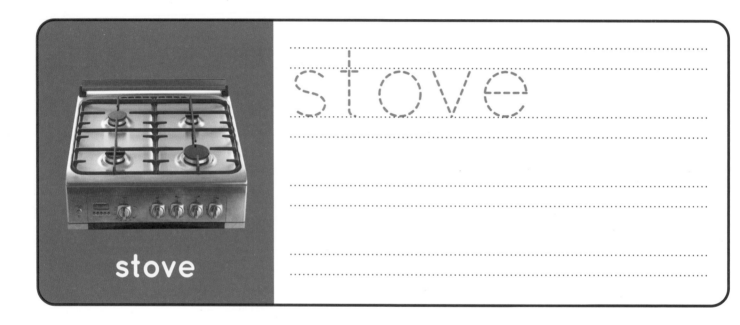

stove

stove

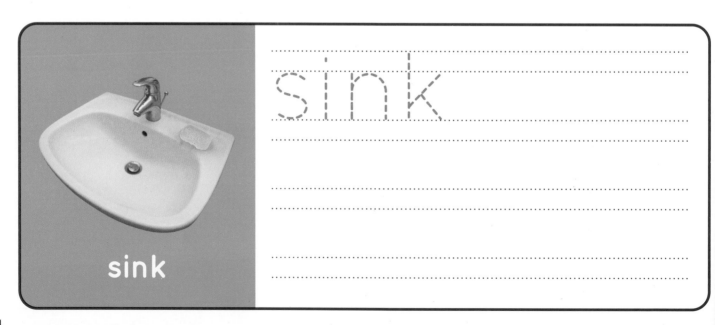

sink

sink

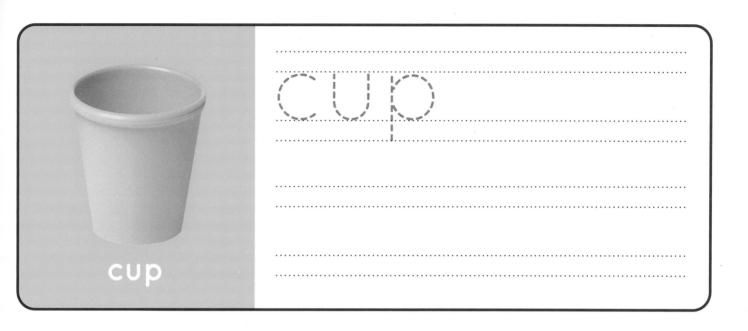

cup

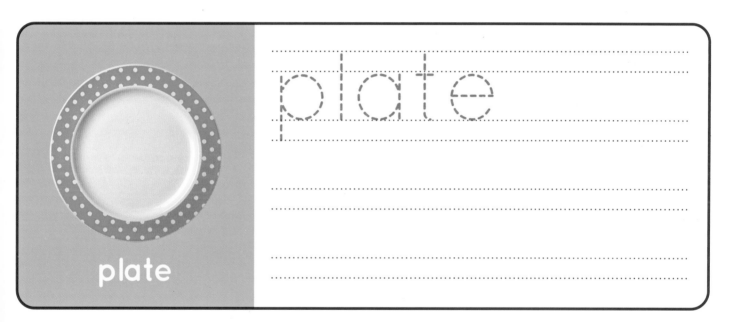

plate

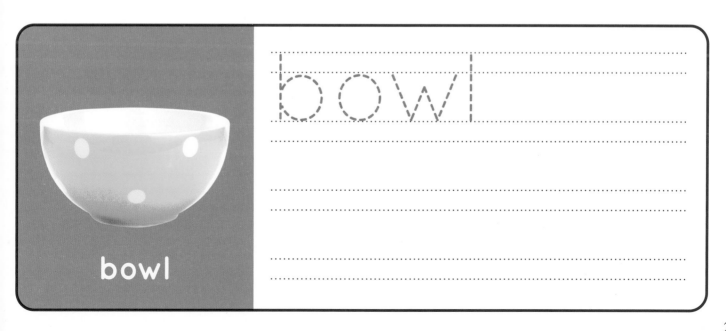

bowl

spoon

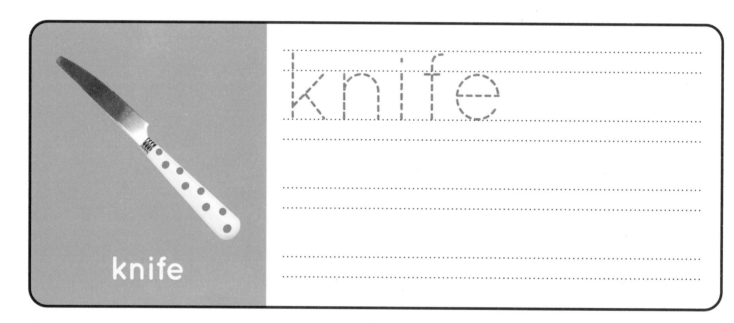

knife

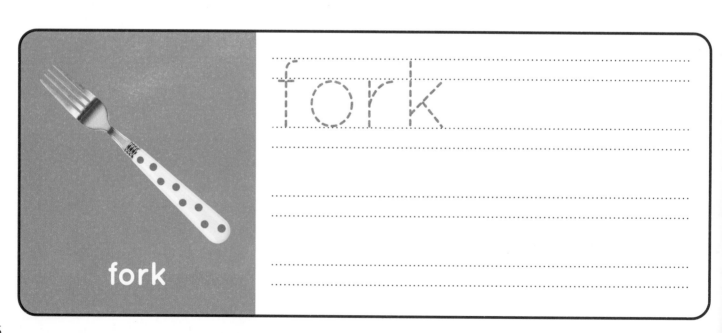

fork

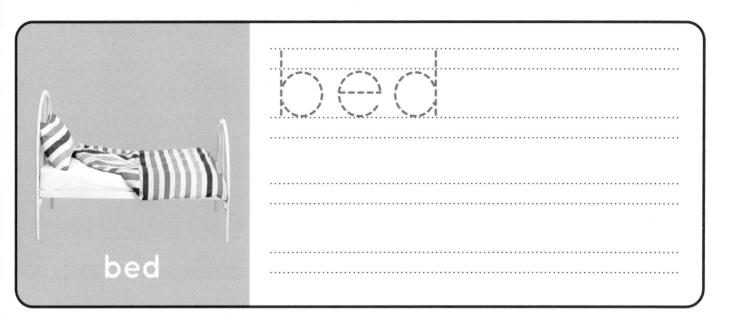

bed

bed

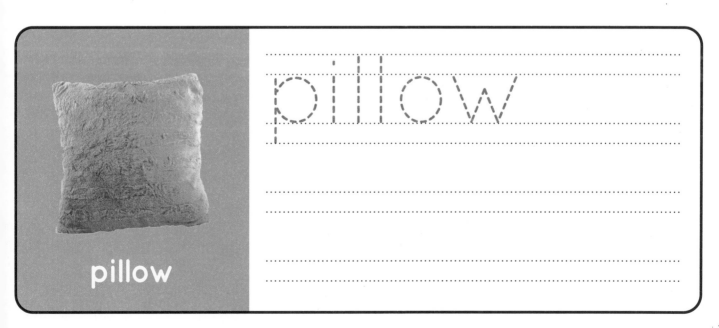

book

book

pillow

pillow

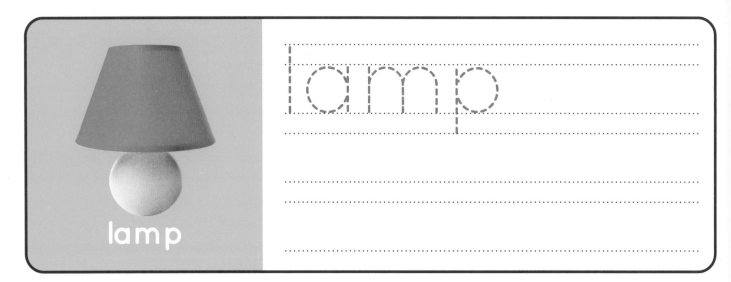

lamp

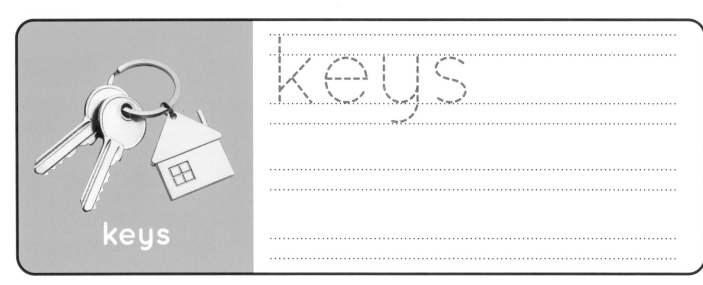

keys

Circle the words below that are found in your bedroom.

sink   bed   lamp

pillow   car

monkey   elephant   book

Spelling

Can you remember all the words you just learned?
Look at the pictures below. Now, write the words that you
can find in your home. Keep practicing until you get it right.

door

CLOTHES

CLOTHES

pants

pants

shirt

shirt

coat

coat

hat

hat

gloves

gloves

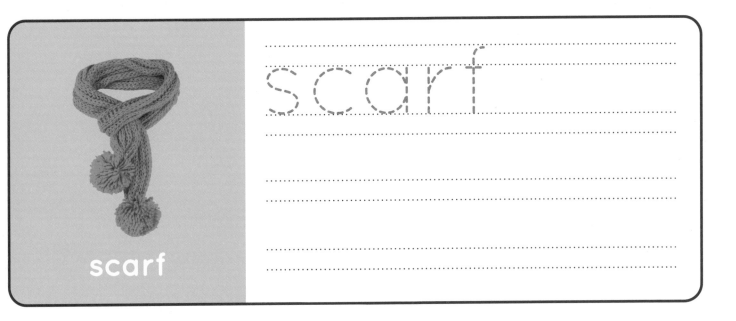

scarf

scarf

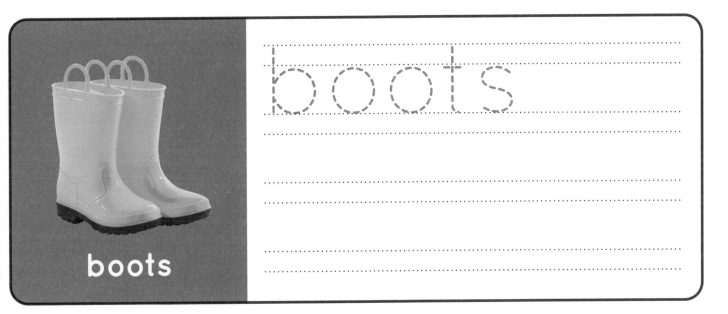

boots

boots

shoes

shoes

socks

socks

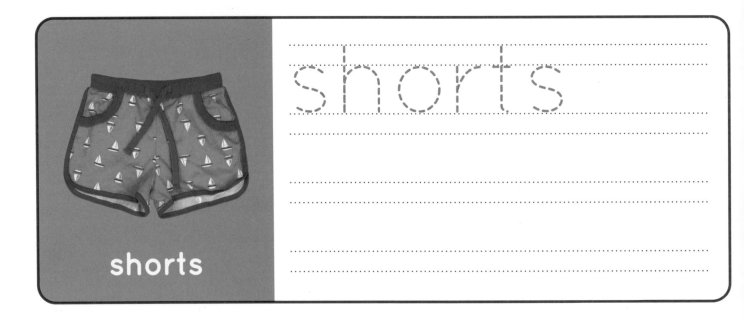

shorts

shorts

tank top

tank top

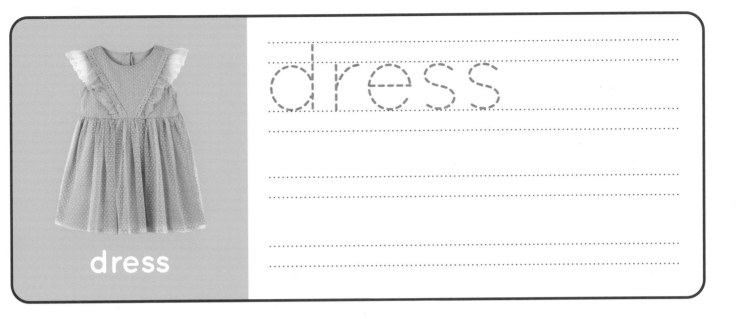

dress

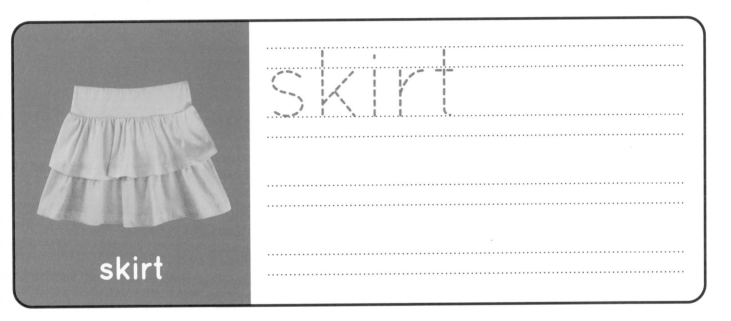

skirt

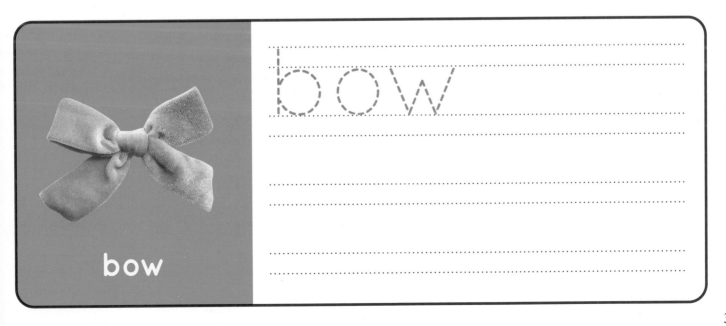

bow

pajamas

pajamas

slippers

slippers

underwear

underwear

Spelling

Can you remember all the words you just learned? Look at the pictures below. Now, write the words of things you wear. Keep practicing until you get it right.

gloves

OUTSIDE

OUTSIDE

sun

sun

tree

tree

grass

sky

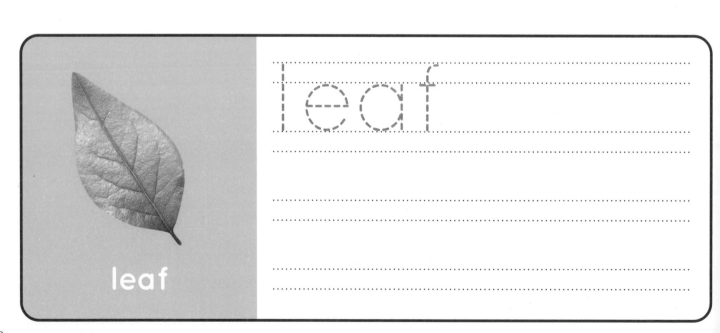

leaf

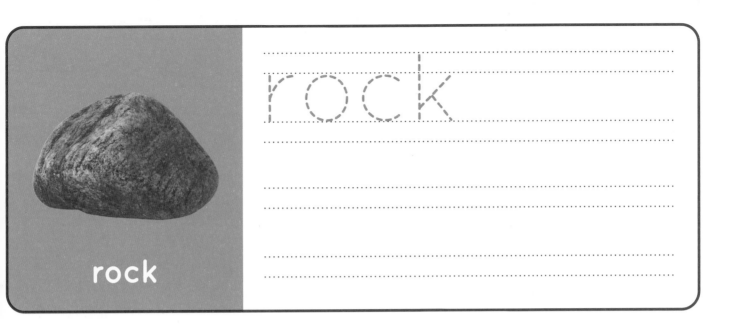

rock

flower

dirt

bird

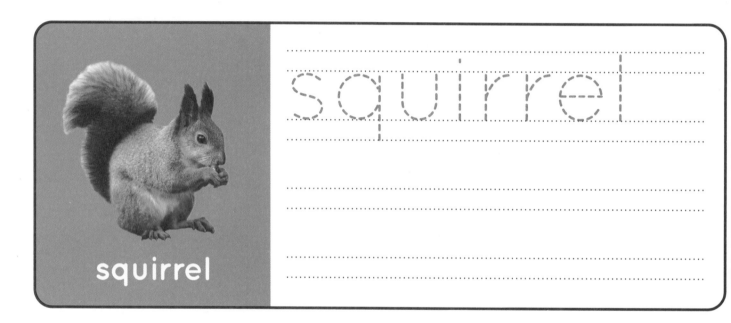

squirrel

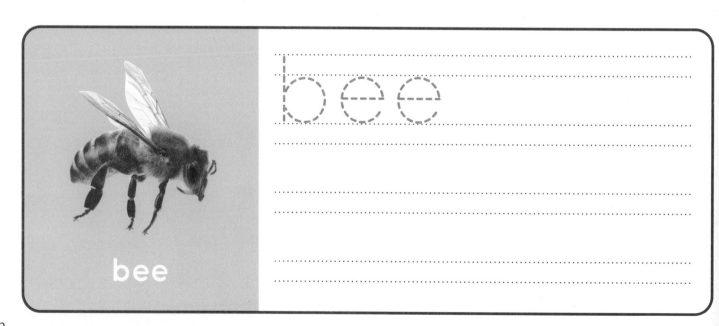

bee

butterfly

butterfly

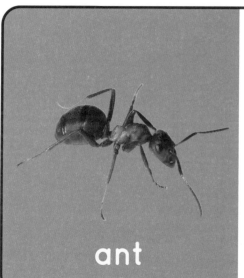

ant

ant

spider

spider

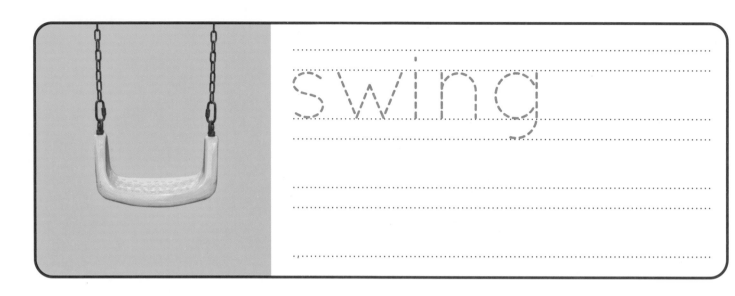

swing

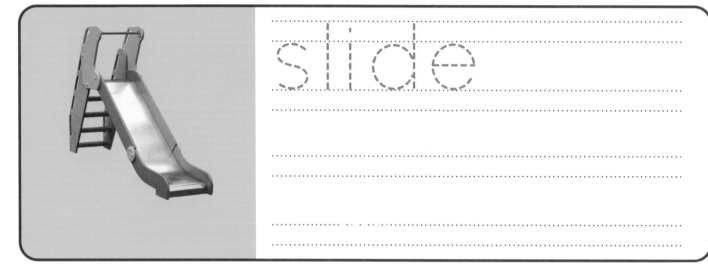

slide

Circle the words below that are found outside.

flower   bed   milk

ant   bird

grass   couch   sink

Spelling

Can you remember all the words you just learned? Look at the pictures below. Now, write the words that you can find outside your home. Keep practicing until you get it right.

squirrel

THINGS THAT GO

THINGS THAT GO

car

car

truck

truck

tricycle

t r i c y c l e

bicycle

b i c y c l e

motorcycle

m o t o r c y c l e

48

tractor

tractor

bus

bus

train

train

ambulance

ambulance

fire truck

fire truck

police car

police car

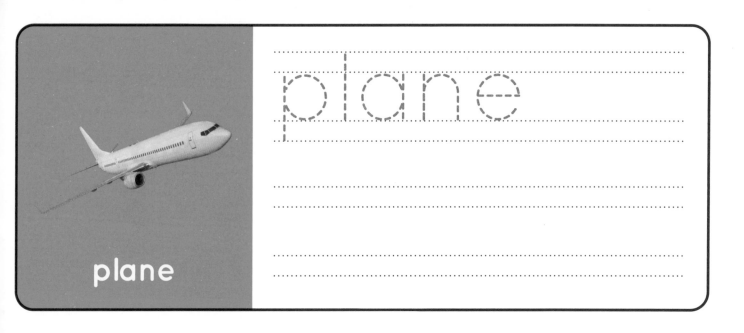

plane

plane

helicopter

helicopter

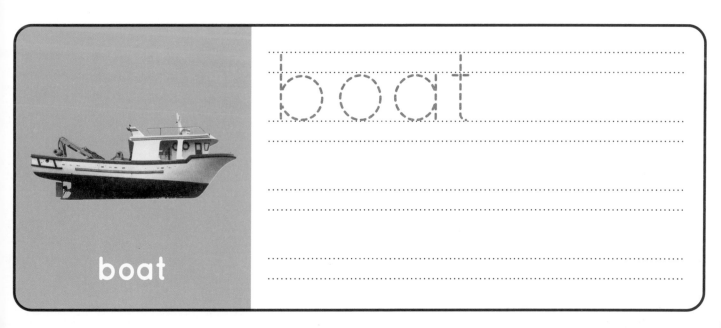

boat

boat

Spelling

Can you remember all the words you just learned?
Look at the pictures below. Now, write the words of the
things that go. Keep practicing until you get it right.

car

Practice Page

Have an adult create exercises for you to complete.

ACHIEVEMENT AWARD

This certificate is presented to

tricycle

for completing and doing a
wonderful job learning 100 first words.

Little Hippo
Books

Sign up to see what's new at littlehippobooks.com

Follow us on social media to stay up to date on the latest from Little Hippo Books

 @LittleHippoBooks

 @littlehippobooks

 Little Hippo Books